RUSTY'S RETURN

By Graham Appleton

Illustrations by Sally Bell

Published by:
British Trust for Ornithology
The Nunnery
Thetford
Norfolk
IP24 2PU

Esmerelda is leaning over the gate chewing her breakfast.
She is looking forward to spring, when the grass will grow and she can get out into the field.
"Mooo, it's cold", Esmerelda sighed.

Daisy joined Esmerelda. "I spy with my little eye, something beginning with **D**", said Esmerelda.

"Duck", replied Daisy.

Mrs Duck and her one, two, three, four, five, six, seven .... eight ducklings all dash past on their way to the pond.

"My turn now", said Daisy. "I spy with my little eye, something beginning with ....**R**".
Esmerelda looked up and there, flying low over the yard, was Rusty the Swallow.
They were both surprised to see him.

"So pleased to see yooooo", mooed Esmerelda. "Where have you been?"

"I've flown from Africa", said Rusty, landing on the gate for a rest. "It was a long way and I am very, very tired".

Rusty told Daisy and Esmerelda about his adventures.

It was a long story and, by the time he had described the friends he had met, the hot sun of the desert, the Camel with a hump, the Lion which roared and about all the thousands and thousands of other Swallows in South Africa it was getting late.

"Time for bed", he said.

Rusty flew into the barn to see if his parents were there.
There were no other Swallows anywhere and Rusty felt very lonely.
He landed next to his old nest and went to sleep.

In the morning Rusty awoke, cold and hungry.
Outside the barn, everything was white and frosty.
Rusty shivered.
It was too cold to find insects.
"Where is everybody?", he said to himself.
"Am I the only Swallow in Britain?"

Rusty looked for flies everywhere, flying round and round the farm.
Ned, the farm pony, felt very sorry for him.
"You may find some flies in my stable", said Ned.
"Thank you", said Rusty.
He swooped in through the door and caught a juicy, big fly.
"Breakfast at last!"

Rusty was feeling much happier.
He landed on the stable door.
The sun was shining now and Rusty looked very smart, with his fine, long tail and his glossy, blue feathers.
He chatted to Ned and wondered where his parents were.

Suddenly, Rusty stopped talking.
What was that? Could he hear other Swallows? He hoped so.
It was lonely being the only Swallow on Honeysuckle Farm.

He flew out into the farmyard and round the corner.
There, flying around the weather vane, were his parents!
"Hello Rusty", they called.

Rusty landed next to his parents. They were happy to see him.
"Where are you going to build a nest Rusty?", his Mum asked.
"Have you found a home?"

Rusty knew the very place to build a nest.
He flew back to see Ned.
"Can I build a nest in your stable?"
"Of course you can Rusty", said Ned, "It gets very lonely here on my own".

Now all Rusty needed was a Swallow to share his stable.
He sat on the roof and sang as loudly as he could, hoping that another Swallow would hear him.
He sang for ages and ages and ages.

Rusty was sad. He liked his new home but he was lonely.

"I spy with my little eye, something beginning with **S**", said Ned.
Ned was right. Coming towards the stable was another Swallow.

"Hello. My Name is Ruby. What's yours?" she asked.

Ned smiled a pony smile.

"This story is going to have a happy ending", he said.

Information for the reader

Rusty's Return is a story. People who have studied Swallows will notice some differences between fact and fiction!

Most Swallows which reach this country at the end of their first winter do return to the general area in which they were raised. In this book Rusty returns earlier than his parents. In fact, we know that adult birds usually return before less-experienced birds so Rusty might not have expected to reach Honeysuckle Farm first. As with many species, males reach their territories before females so it is unlikely that both of Rusty's parents would have arrived at the same time.

Successful migration is all about good timing. The start of spring is variable between years and recent studies suggest that it may be getting earlier. The average arrival date of Swallows is also getting earlier. When they set off from South Africa birds are unlikely to be able to judge how warm it is going to be in Britain in a particular year. As a consequence, Swallows which arrive in March in a cold spring, when there are few insects, may well die. However, in a warm spring, they may be able to start breeding earlier and raise three broods instead of two. If you have Swallows breeding nearby and you would like to help us collect information on nesting success then you could join the BTO's Nest Record Scheme.

Swallow numbers are very variable throughout Britain and Ireland. There have been major declines in some areas. Swallows need three things if they are to breed successfully - somewhere to nest, materials to build a nest and a ready supply of flies. Nest sites are usually in open sheds, stables or barns, many of which have been demolished or turned into homes. With fewer cattle and 'improved' agriculture there is less mud to be used as nest-building material and fewer insects. It is difficult to supply flies but a muddy puddle in a corner of a farmyard might be just what your Swallows need.

If you would like to know more about migration then you may wish to buy *The Migration Atlas: Movements of the Birds of Britain and Ireland* (published by Poyser - Autumn 2002), a landmark publication summarising decades of BTO ringing and recovery records of 188 species. Text, maps and graphics explore and explain all that we know about the migration patterns of British birds.

By buying *Rusty's Return* you have helped to support the BTO's Swallow Appeal, funding research into Swallows and migration. For more information about bird ringing, nest recording and other BTO activities please see the BTO website **www.bto.org** or write for membership details to Sue Starling, BTO, The Nunnery, Thetford, Norfolk, IP24 2PU.

Graham Appleton